THROUGH
THEIR EYES

IMMERSED IN VERSE

Edited By Kelly Reeves

First published in Great Britain in 2020 by:

Young Writers
Remus House
Coltsfoot Drive
Peterborough
PE2 9BF
Telephone: 01733 890066
Website: www.youngwriters.co.uk

Printed and bound in the UK by BookPrintingUK
Website: www.bookprintinguk.com
YB0451G

FOREWORD

Since 1991, here at Young Writers we have celebrated the awesome power of creative writing, especially in young adults, where it can serve as a vital method of expressing strong (and sometimes difficult) emotions, a conduit to develop empathy, and a safe, non-judgemental place to explore one's own place in the world. With every poem we see the effort and thought that each pupil published in this book has put into their work and by creating this anthology we hope to encourage them further with the ultimate goal of sparking a life-long love of writing.

Through Their Eyes challenged young writers to open their minds and pen bold, powerful poems from the points-of-view of any person or concept they could imagine – from celebrities and politicians to animals and inanimate objects, or even just to give us a glimpse of the world as they experience it. The result is this fierce collection of poetry that by turns questions injustice, imagines the innermost thoughts of influential figures or simply has fun.

The nature of the topic means that contentious or controversial figures may have been chosen as the narrators, and as such some poems may contain views or thoughts that, although may represent those of the person being written about, by no means reflect the opinions or feelings of either the author or us here at Young Writers.

We encourage young writers to express themselves and address subjects that matter to them, which sometimes means writing about sensitive or difficult topics. If you have been affected by any issues raised in this book, details on where to find help can be found at
www.youngwriters.co.uk/info/other/contact-lines

CONTENTS

Holy Cross College, Bury

Hadiya Ali (17)	71
Phoebe Collier (17)	72
Ahsan Anjum (18)	74
Charlotte Trenbath (17)	76
Megan Nuttall (17)	78
Leah Alicia Aspden (18)	80
Sami Ladds (17)	82
Elle-Sue Calderbank (17)	83

Loreto College, St Albans

Kate Burke (11)	84
Isabel Pooley (12)	87
Chiara Lomuti (13)	88
Phoebe Roberts (13)	92
Lottie McCallum (14)	94
Alessia Risoli (11)	96

Newark Academy, New Balderton

Alfie Town (12)	97
Charlotte Lake (13)	98
Dominic Collier (11)	100
Archie Smith (13)	102
Jay Charles (12)	104
Alona Sergeicika (13)	106
Toby Lambert (12)	108
Macie Welshman (12)	109
Libby Duddles (13)	110
Amelia Smith-Cowling (13)	112
Ella Gilfillan (12)	113
Cameron-Lee Dunn (12)	114
Jamie Sanders (12)	115
Nathan Binns (12)	116
Rhiannon Brown (12)	117
Oliwia Wojajczyk	118
Gracie Watkin (12)	119
Fin Charles (12)	120
Olivia Sayers (12)	121
Ryley Picker (12)	122
Ellis Hall (12)	123
Jamie Briers (12)	124

Tyler Dodd (13)	125
Emma Taylor (12)	126
Daisy Pounder (13)	127

Settle College, Giggleswick

Raven Coward (11)	128
Lucy Mason (12)	129
Willow Coward (11)	130
Henry Pain (12)	131
Emily Scott (13)	132
Aaden James Ford (11)	133

The JCB Academy, Rocester

Ben Charlie Sharpe (14)	134

Wallington High School For Girls, Wallington

Daania Abuthaheer (12)	136
Bonnie Witter	137
Sivaranjini Pillai (11)	138
Jasmine Williams (12)	139
Ollie Thorneloe (13)	140
Beatrix Leeming (11)	141
Sreeranjini Pillai (11)	142
Anika Gupta (11)	143

THE
POEMS

The Penny

I open my eyes to the conveyor belt,
Where I am put into a group, there I felt,
The warmth of my friends as I knelt,
I am lucky, some go down the highway and some go melt.

Stress of my shoulders, stress out the way,
I chatted to my friends before they say.
"Just a few more minutes 'til we lay
In the pocket of the man, hip hip hooray!"

A huge hand grabbed me
And I came out to London with glee
I see the London Eye, Big Ben, Tower Bridge, yippee!
And then the man definitely, but accidentally, dropped me!

I am sad, I am alone, I am hurt, I am scared
As I yell with my loudest Queen Elizabeth voice to be heard
No one heard, the megaphone has just blared
That the Eurostar train to Paris had just been cleared.

A girl picked me up and shoved me to a man
They ran and ran and got on the train and sat next to a fan
We arrived in Paris and I was dropped again
Into a drainpipe and I arrived at my conveyor belt and I
started again.

R'wan Robertson-Yebovi (12)
Claremont High School Academy, Kenton

The Beings Who Took

Today I dine, feasting on food many have stated I require,
However, the memories of my past, I recall
Shall swarm my exhausted mind for eternity,
Let me enlighten you of the story of my world.

Cold sweat descends down my fatigued and shivering body,
I cling onto Noor, my dearest and most beloved companion
I gaze up, eyes bulging in terror
Dilapidated buildings surround me.

My mother exclaims, "Samir, we must make haste!"
I instantly notice her concerning tone
Our village is no more
A utopia that crumbled into ashes
It is time we depart.

To a new home where all beings are seen as equal
From one haven to another
Like a majestic bird would do
Soaring through the air
Roaming the skies, seeking shelter
As to flee the frigid, winter blizzards.

Many have informed me of its royalty
How education holds great power
All for the price of nothing
I seek a new beginning
As my old life has concluded.

The journey was treacherous, revolting and wearying
An incredible bore.

Soon we reach a channel
After this, we will be free
Or so we had thought.

I refuse to share the events that occurred on that stormy
night
Only I had made it onto the shore
Noor in my hands
If I could I would
Exchange a bear for my mother.

My family look over me today
However, I will never see them again

This began with an abundance of people
The beings who took.

Hesham Ghulam Ghulam Habib (13)
Claremont High School Academy, Kenton

When You Look At Me...

When you look at me,
What do you see?
Doctor? Scientist? Maths genius?
Why am I not just a child?
Why do you assume, based off my place of origin?

When you look at me,
What do you think?
Housewife? Immigrant? Foreign?
Why am I not just a girl of colour?
Why do you let my nationality choose my future?

When you look at me,
What do you assume?
Gay? Unmanly? Weak?
Why am I not just an aspiring actor?
Why do my choices affect your opinion?

When you look at me,
What do you see?
Laziness? Worthless? Burden?
Why am I not just going through a hard time?
Why does my lifestyle affect my status?

When you look at me,
What do you see?
Attention seeker? Faker? Soon-to-be-dead?

Why am I not just a person?
Why does my mental health define me?

When you look at me,
What do you assume?
Criminal? Drug dealer? Gang member?
Why am I not just a man on a walk?
Why do you let my race decide for you?

When you look at me,
What do you think?
Different? Not needed? Disappointment?
Why am I not just someone in love?
Why do you decide by sexuality over personality?

Why you look at others,
Why do you assume?
Peace of mind? Force of habit? Fixed mindset?
Why can't we all just be equal?
Why do you decide for others?
Why? Why? Why?

Jiya Bakrania (13)
Claremont High School Academy, Kenton

Why Me?

How ironic you tried to ruin me
It wasn't too late until everyone could see
Your evil thoughts, your evil mind
What were you thinking, you evil kind?

You let me in, you made me smile,
What was I thinking? I should have run a mile,
You preyed on me for many years,
Played your games that ended in tears,
You waited for me to leave, so you could take your lead
Turned people against me, to fulfil your evil needs.

I return each day thinking everything's okay
But the day came where your hate turned into rage
For many years, I didn't see you hated me
What? Because I was me!

You watched me every day and befriended me
To only know you wanted to destroy me!
You listened to my stories like a friend
But only to know you would twist them again
The past unfolded, your lies were exposed
And now everyone knows.

You wanted my life, you wanted me to be out,
So you could finally say, I have some clout!
Why the hate? I ask myself, I was just being my jolly self
Questions, questions in my mind,

Will always haunt me, all of my life!
Leave me alone, if you really hate me
Just don't plot your lies against me.

It's not my fault how God created me
We're all different so just let it be!

Saniya Mazhar (12)
Claremont High School Academy, Kenton

Drugs

I see you at your worst
Dying, crying, lying in a bed
They may think I am a curse,
But you will use me and throw me away just like you said.

I will come again,
When you're down again,
Think I'm a curse again,
Throw me away again,
But this time you could not let me go!

I make you feel so high,
Even when you're at the bottom,
Even though it is a lie,
But then you go numb.

We were the best of friends,
Smoked, snorted, drank
Though when I think of it, I just drew a blank,
It is all just a blend.

I tell you to have some,
But you're numb, gone,
I thought I'm the cure,
I guess I am the end.

Now I have the illness,
Now I am the patient,
And there ain't no prescription,

It was all over too,
Though that's all I knew.

I'm no longer numb so I feel the pain,
Please just throw me away,
Again, again, again,
But you still go numb,
Gone forever,
I am the worst, your worst,
That itch for the stuff
That will never go.

Darius Okome (12)
Claremont High School Academy, Kenton

Green Hope

A bird lands on one of my branches,
Rare as I don't see many
It chirps away like most
Fearing the worst
Tick tock.

It doesn't rain anymore
And when it does, it's brutal
The climate changes, capable of the irreplaceable
Tick tock.

The air gets toxic as the days go by
Please give me a chance
For a better life
To prove myself
My powers
My worth
My time is going
Unknowing
Tick tock.

Time passes all the same
My job seems harder every day
Too much CO_2 in the air
I don't know how to bear
Tick tock.

I warned my fellow friends
Yet, my pulses aren't enough
These humans won't listen, they are just too rough
Tick tock.

A truck passed today
My time has come
My efforts aren't enough
Let's hope to find a diamond in the rough
My world is being destroyed
And so am I
Please listen to my cries
To help, to prosper
Yet, you're just a waste
Of space
A disgrace
Tick tock...

Melissa Tiganus (14)
Claremont High School Academy, Kenton

Coronavirus

I started blind, flying around with only my ear,
Dead, I've been killed and going to be eaten,
Arrived in China and now I am here,
In another form and won't be beaten,
I begin my phenomenal journey,
You thought I was something small, but you were wrong,
Going through people's bodies, making sure they can't breathe,
I will have no mercy.

I spread through the air
Touch me, taste me, breathe me, you will die
When you get me, you won't get rid of me
You'll be left decaying in quarantine until you're forgotten about,
There's no way out,
Only one cure that no one has a clue about.

I begin to spread around the world,
I don't think anyone else will be able to cope,
If you touch me, you better wash your hands with soap
Eventually, no one will be left over
Wait, was that a cough?
Well, now it's time
I'll surge through your body and take over
Now for you,
It's game over!

Ayush Patel (13)
Claremont High School Academy, Kenton

Rosa Parks

This is me, Rosa Parks
I grew up near Montgomery, Alabama
I was very brave and I always tried to do what was right
When I was young, my grandparents told me stories of
slavery
When black people weren't free to live like other people
Slavery was over now, but times were still hard for me
Us, black people, were treated badly and were not equal to
whites
I knew this wasn't right
I know I'm just a regular person, just like anyone else
I started working, trying to get more rights for us
I knew what to do, fight
I was sick of rules, that I knew were wrong
I was taken to prison, but I wasn't scared
I knew what I was doing was right
I travelled the country to convince people to join the fight
Finally, after one year, the Supreme Court were going to
change the rules
I fought for voting and women's rights
I was told I was a hero
But I knew who I was
A regular person, just as good as anyone else.

Denisa Toader (12)
Claremont High School Academy, Kenton

Through A Foster Kid's Eyes

The world has no colour anymore,
My life is done and I can't take no more,
Without my parents, my heart is rotten,
I am sure they will never be forgotten,
I am a foster kid who's always sorrowful,
And I would never ever in my life be hopeful.

The roses have gone black,
My memories with my parents would never come back,
I see many kids with their mum and dad,
And just there, I start to get stabbed,
The world has no colour anymore, it has all faded away,
I am dull and I never play.

My parents left me alone in this big world,
All I can do is cry and learn,
My face has gone grey because of all those tears,
But no one around me really cares,
I have nobody in this life,
And all I can think of is holding a knife.

Sometimes I feel like committing suicide,
But because of my parents, I've already died,
No other family can replace my beloved parents.

Imaan Amanzai (12)
Claremont High School Academy, Kenton

Inside The Earth

I'm not perfect, not even close,
Humans think I like to be their host,
I get beaten and bashed every day,
How bizarre, I don't even get paid!
Eight billion years without a friend,
I sometimes worry about my end,
Humans will only speed up the time,
Even when this is my first rhyme.

I am just a rock with a molten core,
Humans want more, but I'm getting sore,
I imagine a planet with plants to live on,
That's where I would like to be,
Then I would finally be free,
I would rather be the burning, hot sun,
Because I wouldn't have a job to run.

Not all animals are to blame,
Mostly humans are the main, shame shame shame!
Humans got fine,
And I got called a liar,
If you haven't noticed yet, I am the Earth,
And I have been it from birth,
What I am trying to say, is that I am a rock,
And not to be treated as a dirty, old sock.

Anish Khatri (12)
Claremont High School Academy, Kenton

Through Our Eyes

Until morning comes... darkness,
Opening, but blinded by the sun's sharpness,
We catch a glimpse of fluttering eyelashes,
Covering us like beautiful arches,
Curtains to the soul,
Protecting is their role.

Once we're open wide,
We show our pupils out with pride,
So much goes through us all the time,
Messages to the brain in continuous rhyme,
In the morning and the evening,
We quietly whisper, we quietly sing.

"We're your eyes, giving you sight,
Like shiny orbs with our light
We stare, but never meet,
With a meaning wild and sweet,
Every day as you dream,
Your head fills with a beam."

Every second, we blink blink,
Occasionally we wink wink,
A soft blanket covers us when you sleep,
A night secret it will keep,
Day, after day, after day,
At the end, we lay...

Evangelina Ghinea (12)
Claremont High School Academy, Kenton

Mother Nature

Winter woods now close doors
To the spring tears ahead
Flowers blossom from the shadows
A dance in the breeze now spreads.

Summer love is in the air
The cloudless sky shapes
Memories, paths, wear her green eyes
Bushes now filled with various grapes.

Autumn leaves swift to the ground
Colours filled like fire
Her majesty surrounds the woods
A wind of chill fills the air entire.

Mystical snow sways like glitter
Trees turn like spindly fingers
Her crown filled with bitter twigs
Only a moment will she linger.

Her beauty is so full of life
The gentleness of the sky
The pure sweetness of melody
Is what makes it so alive!

Thadar San (12)
Claremont High School Academy, Kenton

Reality

Imagine being alone, having nowhere to go
Having opps here and opps there and they just won't leave you alone
They wanna see you deceased, covered by dirt and stone
But you wanna live your life, see your brothers rise
And see them covered in riches and gold.

Imagine going pro, only at age fourteen
You don't know what to do because you know your school you'll leave
Imagine being snaked by your own guy as well
Oh well, oh well, cos only time will tell.

Imagine finally realising love ain't really for you
So then you focus on nothing but a great fortune
Imagine the night being black like Zetsu
And someone got put in eternal slumber
Then realising you loved the victim like a brother.

But then there are the real ones
Like 21, KD and Burrito
Oh my God, ain't life funny?
It's crazy how this all got written
In a short space of time
Little did you know, this goes on in people's minds.

Zain Westcarr (14)
Conisborough College, Catford

The Friendly Neighbourhood Spider-Man

As I glide along the abhorrent tracks,
I notice the citizens strolling by,
The shops below glinting in the day's sunlight,
Various people,
Waiting impatiently,
On the station concourse to board me,
Meanwhile,
Below I hear screams like my brakes on an icy morning
I see flames rising vastly
Smoke billowing, clouds consuming my paint
An almighty explosion
Crash!
My rails shake nervously
Panic! Mayhem! Dread! Worry!
Within minutes, what seemed like hours, a familiar figure
appears from the shadows
Spider-Man is here!
He swings in free as a bird, reeking an air of confidence
Saves the public from the blazing inferno
An incoming siren, a clattering of ladders, a troop of heroes
A powerful jet of water and the flames are extinguished
The people down below are relieved
Who is he? Why did he risk his life for us?
In the blink of an eye, he is off again
A dot on the horizon.

Alfie Giles (12)
Conisborough College, Catford

Me And My Best Mate

Hello folks! Woof woof! I'm Ralph,
I'm a guide dog and a best friend to my owner, Thomas
Thomas is an extraordinary person
With a heart of gold, loads of energy and weak eyesight
But I am there for him
Around the house, around the town
Around the whole world
I'm there, his best friend
To guide him through the darkness
To make sure he doesn't fall or embarrass himself
I'm very important to him
I will be there for him
Day, night, evening, noon and early morning and so on
So see me down the street
Don't make fun of me and Thomas
Don't stare, I'm doing my job
I want to help him, he's nice and kind
Not like you staring and judging
This is my story, this is my life
So this leaves a moral
But that's for you to figure out
If you learn nothing, keep reading this
You'll figure it out, woof woof!

Jasmine Watson (12) & Cody Harding

Conisborough College, Catford

Strength And Light

Through your eyes, the lightest bright,
Shines more than the sun, no matter what race,
No matter what religion or views,
I want you to know to stay strong in the blues.

No matter homeless, no matter poor,
Won't ignore when the darkest time comes,
Don't run, shine your light,
Believe for your rights.

And I will fight because there's only one life,
Everyone wants to pursue a goal,
We've seen people kill themselves, give up on life,
But I want all of you to stay strong,
If your dream is to change the planet or help people.

We all should come together
As a nation, no matter
Race, religion or views
Together we can do beautiful things
I believe in you.

Zahndrae Bradshaw (11)
Conisborough College, Catford

Perspective Of The Onlooker

Perspective of the onlooker
Our facade grasps their attention
Enough to make a judgement
A judgement we cannot control.

This judgement is free to interpret
For our mind to ponder on
Our mind will not let the thought escape
Because interaction is based on judgement.

Interaction keeps us sane
It is why judgement always lingers in our mind
We are bound to it
But we don't need to be.

I say we are bound to judgement
But truly, we cling to it
The onlookers' judgement
Their perspective.

We don't need this perspective
We don't need their judgement
We need to let go
Because we don't need the perspective of the onlooker.

Connor George Ennis (14)
Conisborough College, Catford

I'm Going To Die

Espionage is a big crime
It's a shame I have to leave my family behind
I deserve for this to be the end of my time
Not a shameless bone in my body I can find.

I spied on the government and abandoned my family
I really do love them though it's not clear to see.

I'm on death row, my kids will see me die
I did it for the money but now it's not funny.

I only see my family for three hours a week
They won't look me in the eye
My dad can come see me die too
But I don't think he'd like to.

I am devastated to see them go at four and five
Having said that, I'm so very grateful they're alive.

Ruby Cray (14)
Conisborough College, Catford

I Will Never Forget

We were playing at first,
But someone dared him,
To insult me,
So I said something back,
It wasn't that bad.

He looked at me,
His face went red,
The comment I made,
I started to dread,
People gathered round,
And my smile turned upside down.

They tried to hold him back,
But he caught up,
He swung me onto the floor,
My ankle got caught,
I didn't speak to him ever.

When we were leaving year six,
He sent me a message,
I opened it and it said...

Josharnah Buck Simei (12)
Conisborough College, Catford

Logging In

Logging in, I unlock my darkest fears
Panic attacks, teardrops falling down
No one to help me while I'm here.

Logging in, I unlock my darkest fears
The prettier the face, the more likes you get
Now I know why I don't belong here.

Logging in, I unlock my darkest fears
Cyberbullying tears me apart
Maybe I should get out of here.

Logging out, I am transforming into my darkest fear
The rope is ready, ready for me
I have no reason to stay here
Everything... has gone wrong.

Leira Emmanuel (13)
Conisborough College, Catford

Rhyme

Roses are red
Violets are blue
This is our mix
Just like you.

This is a cover
This is a rhyme
This one is big
It's not a crime.

This is big
This is tall
I am big
Not gonna fall.

You have seen
The best of me,
Please choose me
I am so keen.

Micah Spence (12)
Conisborough College, Catford

I'm Not To Blame

All of this abuse is getting to me a bit you know,
And Graham Souness is making my head want to blow,
When I signed that contract, I read it page by page,
But the last thing I looked at on the paper was the wage,
No, I'm not lying, I'm not being funny,
But the last thing I came here for was the money,
I train very hard and do it all day,
But this British press is making me want to move away,
If all of these people want the club to get rid,
Then fine, I'll fly directly to Madrid,
I don't want to go, I really do care,
It's not all about the cars and my hair,
I went to Russia and won the World Cup,
Just to make these English clowns shut up,
But I am focused, Manchester United is all that matters to me,
When I die, I want bags of respect, just like Kobe,
I want to fill my potential, go down in history,
And nothing matters more than this to me.

Jack Welsh (13)
Harton Academy, South Shields

Our Warming World

The world is warming, the world is crying
Every creature, thing and man is dying
We tried our best to no avail,
To live much longer, we may have to bail.

We still have a chance but not for much longer,
We will take to the stars and start to wonder,
It was going so well but once and for all,
The story always ends with a massive fall.

To find a new home and wave goodbye,
It's our planet and we will try,
Our world is falling and falling fast,
Any of our breaths may be our last.

If we live past the massive disaster,
We will save our world or it'll fall even faster,
No matter what you do is 'the ways of men'
We all have a few years left less than ten.

The problem with that, are the people of greed,
Our cities will fall and their people will bleed
The only way forward is to fight,
So we can help everyone and it's going to be tight.

Our planet may live but we could die,
Burying its secrets, and for years will lie
The governments and armies may be strong,
At the end of the day what they do is wrong.

Fight for yourself and see what you do,
While the rest of the world die from flu,
If we somehow manage to pull through,
The only people left may be me and you.

We think we're in control but we're really not,
The options we have are not a lot,
But all we need is a little time,
And we could save our planet and be quite fine.

Our options are short,
We need to abort,
As the world will end if we don't change,
What I'm going to say may sound strange
We undid ourselves and destroyed our home,
I hope this will get to you my final poem.

McKenzie Davies (13)
Harton Academy, South Shields

Influencers

I'm in this place
It is a disgrace
Bullets fly around us
Dead bodies lie all through the beach.

We hear a noise
"Cover!" one man shouts
A bomb flies over me.

I'm in this place
It is a disgrace
Bullets fly around us
Dead bodies lie all through the beach.

It's dark
I can't see anything
I see other people
People I saw on the beach

I'm in this place
It is a disgrace
Bullets fly around us
Dead bodies lie all through the beach.

I look down
There is my wife
There is no fire
But a smashed house.

I'm in this place
It is a disgrace
Bullets fly around us
Dead bodies lie all through the beach.

The postman arrives
On his bicycle
Brown and rusty
And delivers the package
A gold medal to say I'm dead

I'm in this place
It is a disgrace
Bullets fly around us
Dead bodies lie all through the beach.

There is no place
No beach
No bullets
Only home
Stop fighting.

Elliot Phillips
Harton Academy, South Shields

Pain, Agony, Anxiety

She holds me in her shaking hands
Clenches my handle with all her anger
She tries to scream, she tries to hide
But the conflict is locked inside.
She slits her arm because no one's there,
Her friends and family won't even care
She laughs and smiles to conceal the pain
She plunges me inside, again and again
She thought no one was there, her parents asked her if she
was okay
They never thought to ask twice, until...
They saw her with a knife
Her blood dripped against my blade, I committed the crime
And never got to say goodbye
I saw the grief in her eyes and heard her parents' cries
Her brain caused her too much trouble, this overwhelming
pain
Would never go away, like a looming shadow
She thought what was better
A life with sustaining grief
Or a death with internal relief?
Behind locked doors, her parents scream her name
But no answer would ever be heard again
My blade covered in blood, I dropped to the floor

Pain
Agony
Anxiety.

Aneesa Choudhury (13)
Harton Academy, South Shields

Soldiers

As the night did bleed into light,
I saw my soldiers standing together
As a house and each man a brick.

Most would see a sight of men
Who were ready to fight
But all I saw was a battalion
Of painted lambs in a field
And a farmer with a knife.

Oh, did I cry this day?
But did I cry a tear in vain?
Or is it my own extruding pain?
Or is the longboats out of sight,
Which would bring these soldiers to the light?

The pain I feel inside is nothing
To the real monsters that lurk over the tide,
In boats of shields, and hearts
Of knives and swords and mace
These are the savages we must face.

Some men so young
To have ever even had a wife
Will be snuffed out as if a light.

Their wick is still so long
But this will be their final song
As each man in a standing line.

But this is a pain I bear alone
Mustn't dwell on what atrocities they could do
Or how this may be our last battle
Before we rot in our own tomb.

Robert Bilton (14)
Harton Academy, South Shields

Dominoes

I walk into school,
Kids, there are tons,
So many different backgrounds,
But when break time comes,
There is one that I see,
And when I see him, he runs.

I chase him and catch him,
And then call him weak,
I don't know why I hit him,
It just helps me sleep.

He doesn't see how it's his fault,
He doesn't see how that's true,
But I punch him in the face,
And spit on him too.

And now I get home,
For a beating of my own,
What comes around, goes around,
And that for sure I know.

I don't see how it is my fault,
I don't see how that's true,
Now my dad opens the door,
He's been downing Malibu,
I really wish my mum was here,
She would know what to do,

But now I have to wipe my tears,
Richard, I hate you.

Jay Robson (13)
Harton Academy, South Shields

The Prisoner

I feel like a prisoner behind bars
Locked up, beaten up with only scars
Dressed up in black and white
I wish people could see my view of sight.

I feel like a prisoner that is forgotten
Why can't I feel the wrath of cotton?
My family, my friends, no one cares
I can't even breathe the solid airs.

I feel like a prisoner, hurt and weak
Depressed and commanded just like a freak
What did I do with my actions?
I regret this, I'd rather solve complex fractions.

I feel like a prisoner full of anxiety
I deserve a better society
What did I do with my life?
Horrible terror and terrible strife.

I feel like a prisoner who can't survive
I'm not alive, I need to be received
This is jail, I can't escape
Never seeing the beautiful landscape.

Taheem Hoque (11)
Harton Academy, South Shields

Football Is Not Everything

I'm not your stereotypical player
I don't want attention
Even though I am the net slayer
And I do like to get redemption
I might be world-class
But I don't want to be called a king
My hometown is my main thing
Football is not my life to me
It is giving the village supplies such as tea
They deserve it more than anything
For all their hard work
I wish I could give them everything
Even though they are berserk
That picture of me went everywhere
With my smashed-up phone
I am the Senegalian bear
My old villagers don't have a nice home
They should be granted education
And many other things
Along with compensation
Because of all the people who gained their wings.

Henri Eddon (14)
Harton Academy, South Shields

Only Sixteen

The noise around me was burning my ears
I couldn't feel anything apart from my tears
My adrenaline was pounding inside of me
I knew that this was just the beginning
But it was the end of he.

There were bombs exploding everywhere
I knew that this just wasn't fair
I was forced into the army at only sixteen
But you will never guess what I had seen
If only it was the end!

I didn't know if my family were safe
But I just had to believe and have faith
I miss my home so much
Oh, what I would do for one more lunch.

A vast pain hit me in the heart
It felt like a sharp dart
Before my eyes, I fell on the ground
Always to be gone but never to be found.

Abbie Saunders (13)
Harton Academy, South Shields

Hi Sisters!

Hi sisters!
I say as I wake up
And I get out of bed today to sell more make-up.

But as I check my phone
I see another scandal
This drama is far more than I can handle.

I rant to my bro
But what would he know
He doesn't even think global warming is real
I search my phone for more content to steal.

I stare up at the sky
And I wonder why, how am I the most-hated YouTube guy?
But then I remember, Jake Paul exists too
So I feel my day start off brand new.

Tati thinks she's so cool, but I'm no fool
She's using me as a subscriber tool.

To gain more and more
Is all we aim for
That is part of the beauty guru law.

Amber Clifton (13)
Harton Academy, South Shields

Anxiety

Anxiety is within each child
A tempered feeling that has gone wild
As you lose your sense each day
Your other feelings just hide and pray
When it attacks, you start to cry
Your sight goes fuzzy and your life's a lie.

Then you realise that it's not real
You wipe the waterfalls and then you feel
Your other feelings have come out again
The fear has left the anxiety train
It left the station to recharge
Through the crowd, it would barge.

As you stare into space
You hear a snap in front of your face
Your family asks if you're okay
You just explain your odd day
Then you feel good for a while
You put on a brave face and start to smile.

Kurtis McAlpine (14)
Harton Academy, South Shields

Something I Loved, Something I Hated

From the age of ten, I turned to music
I love music, music was my life
During the long days, I made videos
Videos of singing, singing something I loved.

From the age of fourteen, I created a song
Ocean eyes, deep blue ocean eyes
Something I loved.

From the age of seventeen, darkness came near
I hid in my shell
I hid with my fear, depression came near
Something I hated.

At the age of seventeen, I had a dream
I was forgotten about as I dropped down, no one cared
Something I hated.

Now I'm eighteen
I got everything I wanted, everything I dreamed of
They were there for me
When I needed them most
Something I loved.

Jannatul Jannah (12)
Harton Academy, South Shields

The Flame

I am a fire, orange and bright
Here to burn everything in sight,
Do you see that tree?
It's there no more,
Because I am a giant fireball.

Embers, embers in the sky,
Just above the burning sight,
Slipping and sliding through the trees,
Coming to burn everything I see.

I am big
I am small
But most of all, I am a fireball.

Here's the town
There are the humans
Can you see the homes of the humans?

I had luck,
That's no more.

I was a fire, orange and bright,
I nearly consumed everything in sight,
Do you see that house?
It's still there
Because I used to be a fireball.

Alexander Defty (12)
Harton Academy, South Shields

The Heart Of Tar

I live down below,
In a place where darkness grows,
Living in lonely pain,
Can make you go insane?

I was not always this way,
I will soon have my day,
Once I had love so deep,
But now all I can do is weep.

She has the most beautiful eyes,
But now I am cut from all the loose ties,
I was deep for my love,
But she flew away like a dove.

Oh, how I miss my old life,
She could have been my lovely wife,
But now I have lost my chance,
So let me have one final glance.

Now I feel like I am being choked,
I have almost broke,
Now I sit here heartbroken,
This is my story, unspoken.

Ethan Carr (13)
Harton Academy, South Shields

Quiet Kids

It's hard, be more quiet
Everybody thinks you're just a lifeless mask
Entertaining school, then just leaving
Not doing much, just sitting there
But that's not what happens.

It's like there are two of you
One shy
One loud
In constant turmoil
Every time a question is asked
When you need to put your hand up
The shy one wins.

The worst thing about it all
Is that you're quiet because you don't know what people
would think
And you don't know what people would think because
you're quiet
It's a vicious circle
One that us quiet kids need to get out of.

Jacob Tebble (14)
Harton Academy, South Shields

My Little Shed

As I sit in my little shed on my bed
With my little window and narrow
Door with a hole through it
Where the wind always blows.

I feel so lonely with
No one to talk to
I only have my books to read
And the horses to feed.

Another lonely day passes.

Oh, how I wish the world would change
But in their eyes, I am very strange.

I don't like this place
Could I leave without a trace
If I leave
There would be no grieve.

I have seen many go
It is all with the flow
Nothing that I can do about it
Sometimes we all have to quit.

Jennifer Webber (13)
Harton Academy, South Shields

What Is Lonely?

I feel like I've been trapped in a cage,
Treated like an animal, I shout with rage
Why do they treat me like this? I wonder
The colour of my skin doesn't define the way I should be
treated
The colour of my skin doesn't make me anymore different
from others.

Away from the men on the ranch
I stay alone, away from all the fun
Away from all the chatter
I mutter day and night.

Some days I wish I had a family
Then I would be able to leave this ranch
No more being lonely
Only treated with love and care
I don't know how much longer I can bear.

Nabiha Ahmed (13)
Harton Academy, South Shields

Left

Screams echoed from the room,
I heard with my plastic face,
It has left an instant doom,
For it did not have any grace.

My owner had cried,
Muffled in his little pillow,
He had wept, he had tried,
I wish I could've helped my fellow.

They had already left,
Glass shattered and doors slammed,
The boy's heart - at theft,
Had been robbed, and taken, and scammed.

But what could I have done?
I was just a plastic, lifeless toy,
All the misery and horror that had gone,
Those parents who left, never said goodbye to the boy.

Benjamin Sanaullan (14)

Harton Academy, South Shields

People Think I'm Brave

People think I'm brave
But really I was just upset
By the way white people treated us
It really wasn't fair.

Someone told me to move
But I wouldn't budge
This time
That had taken it too far.

Lots of people supported me
With my choice
But really I just think
It was unneeded.

People decided to fight
For our human rights
Until we were even
With all our rights.

I'm glad I made that choice
To not give up my seat
Now black people are even with white people
And we now have our rights.

Katie Hunter (14)
Harton Academy, South Shields

A Life Of A Bully

As another day goes by,
My life is always a lie,
I am known as a bully,
And I beat them fully,
As this is a normal day,
No one can stand in my way.

I hate school,
Everybody is cruel,
I make them cry,
Made one of them fly,
Got kicked out of school,
Everybody thinks I'm a fool.

I don't like it here,
I don't want to be here,
All I do is fear,
I want to go out,
But my time is not near,
My life is hell,
This place is like a shell,
Except it's a prison cell.

Habib Ahmed (14)
Harton Academy, South Shields

A Different Kind Of Reflection

As I stared into the distance
I saw something new,
The smile on my face
Have I lost that too?
Those pearly white teeth
That messy brown hair,
Those beautiful brown eyes
That deep, soulful stare.
They left me before
A couple months ago,
Now all I have left
Is my heart and myself.
So hear me here
Loud and clear,
"I will not change
I will not break
I will find myself again."
Those tears I shed
Formed you and me,
And I stand here today
As proud as I can be.

Rabiah Zinat (14)
Harton Academy, South Shields

Living Off Rations!

I was so hungry
My tummy was very rumbly
I've lost all my passions,
As I've been eating off rations.

I was in fear,
I felt like my brain wasn't in the right gear
I feel so sad
I feel like I've done so bad.

I can hear the bombs going off
The pollution of them has given me a cough
The world is turning
My ears are burning.

I used to be able to see the stars,
But as it's gone on they seem so far,
I hadn't prepared,
And it's making me scared.

Emma Cox (13)
Harton Academy, South Shields

Endangered

E very night my family die,

N o, they never do say goodbye,

D ays don't go past where I do not cry,

A nd all of my life has been a lie,

N ever goes a day in my life, where my home does not die,

G reen palm trees fade away, all because oil makes your stomachs fly,

E very night, the end becomes nigh,

R age is the only thing that will fly in the sky,

E very day, more than a thousand of my brothers die and die,

D o you not care about the orangutans?

Tahrian Chowdhury (14)

Harton Academy, South Shields

A Prisoner's Life

Alone at night, behind these cold bars,
Keeping me awake with the sound of police cars,
My day of death is set,
For a prisoner is not what I want to be.

Screeching sounds of car engines
Coming from outside of narrow windows
Imagining sights of green grass and pools
Things I will never get to see.

Lying on my cold, hard bed
The only place I can rest my head.

I lie awake at night
Counting down the days
Until I won't be here,
I never thought I would go this way.

Marley Holmes (14)
Harton Academy, South Shields

The Jungle Life

The jungle lion's roar
As the hunters listen in awe
In the night sky, the doves
Fly high to find their nest
Slightly in the west
Cheaters run fast
They are never last
Deers and doe
Are just too slow and can't
Always hide from the pride
Elephants go stamp and tiny fireflies
Light up like a lamp
The monkeys they swing
While the meerkats do their thing
As darkness falls, the lion calls
One last roar and settles his paws
And I'm just a tree
A palm tree.

Dylan McKeith (11)
Harton Academy, South Shields

Through The Eyes Of The Earth

C O2 emissions rising leads to
L evels of sea rising from
I cebergs melting causes
M ore erratic weather which contributes to
A nimals dying with
T emperatures rising
E very forest shrinking.

C oastlines eroding with
H omes disappearing because
A ll our pollution levels rising and
N atural gases are running out, all because of
G reed from all mankind, our
E arth is in trouble, please help everyone.

Karlysha Pattison (11)
Harton Academy, South Shields

Behind Bars

My home behind these cold prison bars
The noisy engine of police force cars
My day of death is set out for me
But a criminal isn't what I wanted to be.

The piercing sound of wind
Outside the small prison window
I picture the grass and the bees
A sight I might never get to see.

The cold, hard, metal bed
The dreaded day playing in my head.

I stare at the ceiling
Counting down the days
I never even imagined
I would die this way.

Ellen Hood (14)
Harton Academy, South Shields

In The Bars

I've seen everything now,
The anger, the hate, the sadness,
All the emotions,
He came not so long ago,
They say he's a 'murderer' or a 'savage',
But I know he's not,
He's a gentle giant,
Although he may seem violent,
He really just needs someone to love him,
He doesn't know it, but someone does,
That someone is me,
The bars of his cell,
His jail cell...

Bethany Simmons (11)
Harton Academy, South Shields

Prisoner In My Head

I'm a prisoner in my own head,
Nobody can tell,
I spend my hours banging on the walls,
Screaming to escape,
Nobody can hear me,
The words, 'I'm not good enough',
Chasing me around,
Nobody knows my pain,
I fake a smile,
Pretending everything's okay,
Nobody knows I'm slowly breaking,
I try to piece myself together,
Piece by piece,
Nobody knows the pieces fall.

Beth Hassan (12)
Harton Academy, South Shields

Elephants

I am an elephant as big as I can be,
But there is no one else that even looks like me
I have two enormous tusks and a long, long trunk
I eat marulas that make me drunk and furious
Like sometimes when I see my biggest enemy
Humans in my territory
Then I fall over on the ground
With a big, banging sound
My shining, round eyes
They look at the beautiful, blue skies!

Moshiur Mohammed (12)
Harton Academy, South Shields

Friends

Another exhausting day passes by
I think that everyone wants me to die
All of the people I am with are bad
Which is one of the reasons I am sad
I think I need some new friends
Or I think my life might come to an end.

I have never really liked school
Everyone there is really cruel
Every night, my mother gives me hugs
Every day, my friends make me do drugs.

Sam Back (14)
Harton Academy, South Shields

No Way Out

Trapped within my heart is a robin at bay,
It chirps and sings for as long as it may,
I want to let it out but how, oh how would that be?
Not once has anybody noticed me,
I sit there alone with only the friend in my soul,
People's words get thrown at me like fire burning coal,
I stay with myself as there is no other way,
Trapped within my heart is a robin at bay.

Nicole West (12)
Harton Academy, South Shields

Being A Teen: Social Media

I've got lots of people liking my posts
Every day, I get a bunch of texts from people
I get tagged in photos
I get invited to stuff
However, this is not such a dream
I get people coming up to me
Asking for help because of their 'friends'
Stop hiding your identity.

Tasnia Choudhury (12)
Harton Academy, South Shields

The Ocean

I was once happy and loved...
But now my beautiful home, gone!
Colourful coral now dust...
Seeing my beloved creatures dying
Plastic killing the plants, animals and me
Feeling like a bin,
Plastic and plastic every second
Killing everything!
I was once happy and loved...

Dani Richardson (12)
Harton Academy, South Shields

Save Me

I am a lion.

My home is destroyed
Save me.

My family has been killed
Save me.

My territory claimed by man
Save me.

My home is destroyed
My family has been killed
My territory has been claimed.

Save me, please.

Daniel Jones (12)
Harton Academy, South Shields

I'm The Only One Left

I'm the only one left,
I'm all alone,
One tree to another,
We're dropping like stones,
These silly humans,
They're chopping us down,
Soon, it'll be me,
Who falls to the ground,
I'm the only one left,
I'm all alone.

Janey Southerton (12)
Harton Academy, South Shields

Wild Prisoner

I was a prisoner,
I was stuck in a cage,
Like a wild animal.

I was a prisoner,
Staring at the walls,
Day and night,
I hated every day, every night.

Ellie Smith (12)
Harton Academy, South Shields

Help Our Earth

E arth is collapsing
A nimals are dying every day
R ubbish is everywhere
T ime is running out
H urry up, we need your help.

Ellie Clark (12)

Harton Academy, South Shields

I Am A Tiger

I am a tiger
I stalk those who talk
When the birds tweet
I eat my meat
As the sticks below paws
Crackle and crunch
I throw a punch.

Ethan Dixon (12)
Harton Academy, South Shields

My Bush Fire Rage

Humans, the original cardinals of sun,
Lustful beings brimmed full with greed and envy,
Horrifying, yet somehow beautifully bewitching.

I have watched you since the picking of the bloodstained apple,
I have watched you pumping the skies full of poison,
What is your alibi?
You are a hypocrisy, tied up in a neat, little bow and labelled - human.

You use me, tell me I'm a lie,
A false prophecy,
And made my existence,
Why won't you let me rest?
It burns, it burns!

Now my temper is bubbling, growing and evolving,
From a soft amber glow into the roaring jaws of hell.

You have found my hand
Fine, I surrender.

Death uttered tears quickly evaporate into an ashy plague,
Trapping and suffocating tiny lungs
Soft whimpers echo amidst the bush fire rage
Stop
Please.

Hadiya Ali (17)
Holy Cross College, Bury

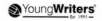

Struggling

The sun rose beneath the thick clouds,
Like a sinner escaping hell, the cries began,
The sleep stopped and the darkness filled.

She carried a weight upon her shoulders,
But a face like hers you'd never know,
A heart that was once so big, now left crumbling,
At the scene, no glue could fix this broken woman,
Nor a man, or child like she supposed.

The walk to nursery is miles and miles in the eyes
Of a broken woman, the pain she feels
When she must let her go, is like giving birth all over again,
You take that pain for a lifetime of happiness
But was it worth it?

Now this broken woman with no feelings at all,
Lies in a house that isn't hers, surrounded by people,
By thoughts that she didn't even know existed.

A once-happy woman who strolled the Earth,
Now trembling at the thought of leaving this house,
She takes her phone and scrolls through torture,
Friends posting pictures of college, people laughing, people
growing,
And she's stuck in this God-forbidden house,
Whose fault is this?

If she lay there any longer, she'd become a stone,
The pen flowed with the words on the tear-ridden page
Her mind blank, her heart no longer existing.

She soon found herself standing there,
Cars passing, people watching, police sirens
In the distance, all it took was one stop.

Her eyes began to wake
Her pain began to rise,
And doctors began to arrive,
The rest was history.

Phoebe Collier (17)
Holy Cross College, Bury

Moonlit Night

One night,
I saw a pair of lovers escape a grey city and into a
wilderness of fireflies
One soul enthralled by the other, as they entered the
embrace of the woods.

My curious eye followed them from above
Peeking through the leaves to observe the magic they would
create
In their newfound heaven together.

Hand in hand, they rushed across the grass
and sung to the tawny owl's music
My light glittering in their gleeful eyes
And I did not know their destination -
Regardless, I followed close behind.

The waded through branches of ticklish fern
And lingered by bushes of fragrant roses
Tumbled down hills like ecstatic children
And I made sure they could see the glow
They manifested in the air around them.

They led me to the shore of a lake
And laid together against a strong, oak tree
Cocooned in each other's arms to watch me dance upon the
waters for them,
Gentle waves glistening, lullaby of ripples
Bringing them to a tranquil sleep.

And there I stayed with them, up above
To guard them from the darkness
And kiss them goodnight.

Ahsan Anjum (18)
Holy Cross College, Bury

Who Am I?

On the top of a cliff
Stands a lighthouse by the sea
Enveloped in my chaos
Aching with vulnerability.

My waves crash with disorder
My lightning strikes above
Remorse is just a concept
As I push and I shove.

Mankind seems so defenceless
Their creation so weak
Merely a child's sandcastle
Washed away nonchalantly.

"We're at the top of the food chain
The greatest predator," you say
And when you kill and steal and conquer
It's easy to think that way.

But your naivety is your hubris
Your inability to be wrong
Because the real, top predator
Surrounded you all along.

I attacked that lighthouse
With no limits or control
The epitome of danger
No sympathy in my soul.

And here I am now
On the 5pm news
Just a form of entertainment
To get rid of your Monday blues.

I lurk outside your window
Ever-presently
As you sit there
Gawping
With lukewarm cups of tea.

And I scoff in disbelief at your idiocy.

Charlotte Trenbath (17)
Holy Cross College, Bury

Your Closest Enemy

Good morning, afternoon, night
The lines are blurred like your memory
My label slowly peeling off
You don't know what I am anymore
I could be poison
Like cyanide, burn your stomach
Kill you with fire
Quickly but painfully
But I am poison
I'm not cyanide
By drinking that, you want the pain
The fire
The end
I'm another type of poison
You use me to numb the pain
Your disappointed parents, your crying children
The wedding ring upon my cork, I'm all that matters
I kill you slowly, without hands or words
On the paper, your name no longer matters
I made you nothing
Cause of death, alcohol poisoning
No wounds
Only a fingerprint upon a glass
I stand upon your grave, alone
Everyone else scared
Leaving only the murder in attendance

But I'm serving my time my friend
And I will take my punishment with no protest
Shackled to those like me, filled with some poison
Ready to repeat my crime for evermore.

Megan Nuttall (17)

Holy Cross College, Bury

The Tracks

Tracks
There's no space, no room, no life
Steht auf!
It's standing or death.

Soldiers
There are men with guns, badges, red
Are they people or animals?
Their smiles make it hard to tell.

Names
We are names, numbers, records
Nummer 6134
Counting was fun but now it's an omen.

Days
The days merge to weeks, months, years
Humans have birthdays
But there's no human left.

Memory
In memory, there is peace, quiet, warmth
Will they remember the tracks
When we're all gone?

Hope
The sky is bleeding. Red, blue, white
Stay alive
In the end, hope is all we have.

God
If there's God, faith, salvation
Heil Hitler!
Then he doesn't know about the tracks.

Leah Alicia Aspden (18)
Holy Cross College, Bury

I Ache Too

Be patient with me,
I wasn't designed for this,
I was designed for more than this,
I was designed for less than this,
I wasn't designed at all,
I was born to watch generations rise and civilisations fall,
I was born to be the battlefield for all of humanity's failings,
I gave you clues,
And you gave me pain,
When turning your weapons on each other became too easy,
You pointed them at me,
Now I burn with the ferocity of the universe,
An inferno, I become
A whole new sun,
You tainted my air with apathy,
Now every breath is agony,
You have walked all over me for the last time,
Atlas is no longer one man,
But legions of children,
Raising me up,
Hearts beating with one purpose,
Be patient with me,
I ache too.

Sami Ladds (17)
Holy Cross College, Bury

Helpless Hopeless

The wind captured the distant memory,
Causing a chill throughout the entirety of my weak,
distraught body
The pretentious face, disguising reality
Depicts wisdom and freedom, yet does it so?

Watching it tear the old reality away...

I sit with the constant reminder of what seemed to be the
perfect life
Talking to shooting stars
But yet, they always get it wrong.

Helpless, with just a torn paper cup, filled halfway with
copper,
The loneliness shredding away at my body.

With no hope left.

Elle-Sue Calderbank (17)
Holy Cross College, Bury

The Eye Of The Bird

A bird closed its eyes and began to dream...
He dreamed that he looked out to a forest,
Autumn had dressed herself for the coming seasons,
donning her vibrant hues
Autumn comes with regal ease,
Content to arrive with slow grace
The trees were full of rusty leaves - red like fire and orange
like a copper kettle - that danced gracefully in the wind,
A single golden leaf pirouetted down an invisible spiral of
breeze, letting itself be carried
Everyone seemed to enjoy the warmth of the autumn breeze
The bird didn't want to leave the forest as it was so calm,
yet full of growth.

He dreamed that he looked out to another forest
However, it looked completely different
He was astonished!
Winter has stealthily crept up on him without the bird even
realising,
Winter had flexed its icy fingers and touched everything in
its path
The forest had a frosty trail and everything was blanketed
by a pure, snowy cape
Winter is such crystalline joy,
Those brilliant rays showing the uniqueness of each and
every snowflake

The whistling wind blew with a powerful passion as if it calls to the spring flowers that will soon bloom
The bird didn't want to leave the forest because it was like a winter wonderland.

He dreamed that he looked out to yet another forest
The spring comes to awake all her children after a long winter
She sends her rain and warm wind to kiss the rich, brown soils,
To waken the seeds and sing to them as they grow.
She blesses the skies with more of our winged animals, from the mighty eagle to the firefly
The flowers come, each one like an idyllic picture-postcard, delicate and strong
And in this time of newness, the bird filled his lungs with fullness and heard her urging him to run,
To feel the power she gives within
Spring was like a developing photograph, the colours deepening with the richness of the season
He had feathers which matched the colours of every tree, of every wisp of wood that promises life to come
The bird didn't want to leave the forest because he loved how it erupted in colour.

He dreamed that he looked out to a fourth forest
A delicious aroma of bread leisurely drifted through the woodland
The amber sun beamed down proudly upon the blissful land
A lake slept in the middle, reflecting the sun's blinding light

A strip of blue sky embraced the clouds overhead like white masses with the aquamarine behind them
The flowers are a new masterpiece each minute, changing the frameless scenery
Summer comes in her own time,
Drifting in on a spring wind, wakening with the kind of warmth that flows to the core,
The water moves softly around the bird's outstretched feathers, caressing smoothly
The butterfly flapped its wings sharply, almost like it was under remote control
It held the stem of the flower and remained perfectly poised by the golden petals which radiated the sun's rays
The bird didn't want to leave the forest, he loved how everything was so admirable.

Kate Burke (11)
Loreto College, St Albans

Eyes Of A Jaguar

S torming through the rainforest, I hear a deadly sound,
A nd everything is falling with a shaking in the ground
V acating my home for no good reason
E xterminating our home, people are treating us with treason.

T ake the word of the jaguar, it's just not fair
H ere we all are taking as much as we can bear
E nemies trying to hide it but everyone's aware.

R emoving all our trees, I just can't take it
A ll our trees will be gone soon, will you commit?
I njuries are common here, not many survive
N eeding help, will you keep us alive?
F reedom we once had is being taken away
O nly you can save us, you'll help us I pray
R escue us before the last tree falls
E xtermination is deadly and to us death calls
S tart preventing this before we are extinct
T ry to stop this because the difference will be distinct
S ave the rainforests before it is all truly gone.

Isabel Pooley (12)
Loreto College, St Albans

Watching Her

Watching,
The rolling waves go by.
Waiting,
As the clock keeps ticking.
Listening,
To the shrieks of the gulls.
No one comes.
No one comes.

"We're near! We're near!"
A man,
Standing.
The boat rocking.
Screams.
A girl shutting her eyes,
Too late.
A man,
Falling.
The sea,
Opening and closing.
A man,
No more.

People arrive,
The question on everyone's face.
Where are they?

Dark, slowly bleeding,
Through the delicate veil of sky.
She loves the here, the now.
Standing on the clifftop,
The sea worships her.
She's at the top of the world.
"Daddy, why are we here?"

A girl clings to her mother,
Humming a tune.
It is a happy tune,
Dancing in her throat.
A happy tune,
For the darkness of the sea.
A dancing tune,
For her mother,
Who rocks.
The tune smiles,
But its mouth is crooked,
And the girl sees it,
Looming,
Sneering,
Mocking.

Her eyelids,
Drooping heavily,
'Til she can fight them no more.
The sound of gentle waves,

Lull her to twisted sleep,
Where words swim,
Back and forth,
Back and forth.
She hears herself.
"Why are we here?"
The reply, a voice, unfamiliar,
"Help me. Help me!"
"Who are you?"
A girl materialises,
Foggy voices behind her.
Panic in her eyes,
Sea in her ears.
Her mouth opens,
A silent scream erupts.
She disappears.

Mind wandering,
To the shore ahead.
Away from here.
To strangers,
With welcome,
On their faces,
On the land.
Waiting,
For her.
To a place of peace.

Away,
From home.
Home.
She clutches her mother.
Tight.
Horror,
As she realises,
Where the boat is going.
Horror,
As she sees
The cliff face,
Slowly crumble.
Horror.
In the eyes,
Of strangers,
With final prayers.

Watching,
The rolling waves go by.
Waiting,
As the clock keeps ticking.
Listening,
To the shrieks of the gulls.
Screaming,
As they struggle on.
And while the world watches,
Help doesn't come.

Chiara Lomuti (13)
Loreto College, St Albans

The Jailer

There are no windows in my cage of steel
No doors either
No light can reach me
I am so used to the darkness, it's like it has its own presence
A perpetual entity, whose existence to me is as normal as
the air or the sky
It's not the darkness which makes my blood run cold
It's the jailer.

She keeps me under lock and key
I hear her voice constantly, dripping with malice and
hostility
Every word sinks in
Like venom is being injected into my blood
I feel it, running through my veins
No matter how hard I try to ignore her
To silence her
She always finds a way of crawling back in
You are nothing, she echoes
You will always be nothing
You don't deserve nice things
You don't deserve your friends
I am doing this for your own good
And how do you repay me?
You are a worthless, ungrateful brat
Why do you deserve to live?

She took my food
She told me I mustn't eat
You disgusting swine
I can't beat the sight of you
Gorging and feasting all day long
I don't know how others can exist alongside you
Without recoiling in horror
Really, you should be thanking me
I'm giving you the chance to undo your gluttony
Surely that's what you want?

I believed this for a while
That this was my punishment
That I was ugly, grotesque, hideous
That, by keeping me here, she was saving my life
I let her lies wriggle their way into my head like little
maggots
Unpicking my thoughts and weaving new ones in their place
Now, I want to escape
I'm tired of her words
I'm tired of seeing the same four walls every day of my life
I'm tired of the darkness
Of knowing that where you are is a million miles from
anyone else
But how can they hear my plea for help
When the jailer is holding my strings?

Phoebe Roberts (13)
Loreto College, St Albans

Martin

My skin crawling, silence entered the room once again,
The atmosphere was dead,
Mum patted the battered, beige sofa,
Gesturing my immediate arrival,
Obeying, my tired legs sprawled across the settee, my head
lay on my mum's lap,
She stroked my thin hair, as I was a child who had just fallen
off of their bike,
A helpless expression blanketing her jade eyes,
Swimming with loss and despair,
"Where's Dad?" I asked,
Voice cracking on the last word,
She took in a sharp inhale,
A thousand knives,
And whispered
"He's gone, Michelle."

For a moment, my mouth hung open loosely,
He'd endured us for fifteen years,
He would have changed my soiled nappies,
He would have braided my greasy hair,
He would have rubbed his rough hand across my rosy
cheeks,
But he was just my dad.

He never picked me up from school,
Or tucked me into my pink sheets,

He never marked his affection on my porcelain forehead,
Or made these bricks less of a cage,
I never dragged him to the cinema or shopping centre,
I never ran into his cold, aching arms as he closed the door,
Because he was just my dad.

Then I was sad,
I remembered how I used to admire him,
I sympathised for the past me,
The disappointment crushing her,
The pressure weighing on her flat chest,
Making her breaths shorter,
And her head pound with confusion,
With anger,
With pain,
For he was just my dad.

The only thing I allowed to worry me,
Was what happened next?
That a few hours ago, I could list everything my dad had
taken away from me,
My hopes, my trust, my life...
After he'd left, my list was completely unfinished,
Because after all,
He was just a selfish guy called Martin,
Who'd taken everything away.

Lottie McCallum (14)
Loreto College, St Albans

Love In Fire

Through her eyes, I can see a world her own
Heart to heart, life for life, like no one has before
A world of her own, special things she can pile
Each one there to make her smile, things from far away...

When it changes, it all goes away
The burn through her heart
I can feel no matter how far away
Worse and worse every day
Fighting throughout their life just to stay awake
Unfair is what it is
Help is all they need to live like us.

Alessia Risoli (11)
Loreto College, St Albans

Life As A Giant

I'm a giant as tall as a tree
I want a friend that will play with me
People assume I'm going ot be scary
Probably because I'm really hairy
Please give me a chance, I just want to talk
To laugh with you or go for a walk.

Being alone for so long has made me quite sad
If I could find a friend I won't feel so bad
Next time you see me don't run away scared
It would be nice to know that somebody cared
I'm kind, I'm gentle, I just want to play
If you know someone lonely please send them my way.

The very next day as I walked from my house
Sitting right there was a little white mouse
I gently crouched down and held out my hand
The mouse scampered upon it just as I had planned
"Please help me," he said, "I can't reach my ball,
It's stuck in the tree and I'm scared I might fall."

I smiled down at him and said, "Show me the tree,
I'd like to help out, let's go, let me see."
I passed out the ball, the mouse shouted with glee
"We'll be best friends forever just you wait and see.
I struggle at times 'cause I'm so small
We're a match made in heaven because you are so tall."

Alfie Town (12)
Newark Academy, New Balderton

Eye Of A Tiger

Eye of a tiger can see you set your heart on fire you big liars you took my family just because we are a different colour

Now the fire rages inside spreading and telling others our differences even though we are the same on the inside

You betrayed us just like you betrayed your souls full of colour now deep inside is only a fire eating the truth

You say we're the devils but look at yourself you're empty puppets being controlled by the lies in this world

Don't let it in your head close the doors instead because the liars are here spreading more fear forever consuming us

Yet you didn't listen and took people's lives now the eye of the tiger is coming you never knew what we were

Because you only judge a book by its cover just like you judged the eye of the tiger now we're coming

To extinguish the fire, we shall go higher and higher 'til you surrender and there's nothing you can do for we are the eye of the tiger

We are stronger than fire we shall become the ones who deliver your soul back to you and make peace

We shall be free you and me and we shall rise above the sea and be free for we are the eye of the tiger

But now you put chains on our wings and trap us, now I see we were never meant to be free unless you can save us and make peace...

You never knew we were the first people to enter Earth, you should have bowed down to us but you just claimed Earth as if you were the one who made this paradise

Now you destroy forests only for you to entertain yourself while we nurture it and try to keep it alive

We are the night we are hidden in the shadows kept safe, you are the day with the sun burning your souls away

How do you feel being the devil's pet? Now normally we wouldn't be so harsh but today is our day, we shall no longer slave away.

Charlotte Lake (13)
Newark Academy, New Balderton

A Dog's Life

I woke up and my mum was there
My brother and sisters too
After two weeks I opened my eyes
And didn't think much of the view

We lived in an alleyway much like a dump
We scavenged the food we could find
And scurried away from the dog catcher's truck
Nearly everyone there was unkind

After some time I was all on my own
My family were no longer there
I was so scared and lonely and cold
I howled at the world, "You don't care!"

Three years went by then along came a man
I really don't trust him, I thought
He gave me some meat and then took me away
Though I growled and I barked and I fought

He took me to sea on a thing called a ship
We went to a strange-looking land
I rode in a van to a nice lady's place
I was still scared so I nipped her hand.

In a couple of days I met with a boy
He seemed to be nice from the start
Although I'd always been frightened of men
It seemed that he had a kind heart

The boy went away but soon he returned
He bought me a bed and a lead
We rode in a car and went to his house
And here I have all that I need

The boy is called Dom and he's my best friend
I greet him when he gets home from school
He brushes my coat and gives me nice treats
He loves me and he's never cruel

I just can't believe how much my life has changed
The end of my trouble and strife
I sleep when I want and have plenty of food
I now really have a 'dog's life'!

Dominic Collier (11)
Newark Academy, New Balderton

COVID Through The Eyes Of Boris

I say, work from home,
Avoid pubs, clubs and theatres,
Don't panic buy.
Some say too late. Some say too soon.
Shelves are plundered of toilet rolls, pasta and rice.
They need to listen!

I say,
Stay at home
Protect the NHS
Save lives
Shops, pubs and schools are padlocked.
Towns and cities hushed.
Roads are deserted.
Thank goodness they listened.

I test positive.
I am taken to intensive care.
Others speak for me.
I hope they're listening.

I say the outbreak is past the peak,
We can start to ease the lockdown,
But social distancing is paramount.
They hear Magic Monday,
Sunbathing and picnics in the park.
Why don't they listen?

I say,
Stay alert
Control the virus
Save lives.
If you can, stay at home.
They say, we're confused,
Some say it's too much, some say it's too little,
Why can't they listen?

I say two metres where possible, or one metre with
protection,
We need to be cautious,
Follow the guidelines.
Thousands protest in cities,
Beaches are congested.
They need to listen.

I say pubs, restaurants and hairdressers can re-open,
Follow the science,
Obey the recommendations,
They hear Super Saturday
Queues stretch for miles.
Trouble's brewing
They must listen.

Archie Smith (13)
Newark Academy, New Balderton

Belief

Life is what you make of it, it only happens once, and there's never a restart button - only a play button
Activities like sports drive you on to be a wiser and stronger person
Some things push you on to do great things
Like being an artist or a runner
But some things that give you that power that have great outcomes for you
like an artist or a runner
Paint the easel as elegant as a swan
If you are a rugby player
Score those tries as rowdy as the Tasmanian devil
If you are anything
You'll definitely have the following:
Responsibility...
Power...
Resilience...
All these things give you the belief to do it
Things may become bad sometimes,
And sure!
Things may put you down when you are alive
But whatever happens
You'll have that self-esteem that will make you strive
As sport is not just an exercise,
It's an all round great thing that makes you strong,
Yet also confident.

But you need to have that self-esteem to help you strive
As everybody has only one chance to make their self
So, what are you waiting for!
Be your much greater self!
Because some things push you on to do great things.

Jay Charles (12)
Newark Academy, New Balderton

A Mess Of A Teenager

They want me to be prepared
For the future that is near,
But the truth is I am scared
Because mine is unclear.

I want someone to hold me,
But I'm the only one here.
I want someone to listen to me,
But I'm the only ear.

The ones who preach friendship
Have left me all alone.
The ones who are not here
Promised not to let me go.

Every word spilled from venomous lips
Attacks the fragile skin and seeps through like a stain.
Words are forever incised.
My heart lies shattered.

Friendship is priceless
And can never be forgotten.
Friendship is timeless
And never rotten.

Fear of love, fear of hate,
Fear of losing my own faith,
Fear of the future, and what it holds,
Fear of growing so cold.

In a world filled with changes
Each and every day,
I feel I'm being judged
For what I do and say.

Now, I lie here in my bed,
My worries slowly eating me.
So many questions in my head
About how my future will be.

It has been so long, moments have wasted!
Fruits of love I have never tasted
Rot on the ground, but will grow towards the sky!
It is the endless circle broken only with goodbye.

Alona Sergeicika (13)
Newark Academy, New Balderton

The Aldred Bat

I unzip my ungainly humungous bag,
The soft sweet scent of linseed oil has been caressed on with a rag.

The bat looks beastly, like a scythe ready to destroy!
I remove it carefully - admire its stature - and plan a bowler to annoy.

I'm next in... helmet ready, pads strapped tight, bat knocked in...
A confident appeal "Owzat!" It's me, I grab my trusted blade and begin.
I practise shots and stride to the middle, take my guard and survey the field.
My bat feels light ready to do battle, today's game result will be sealed.

A 6ft 6" rapid quick bowler steams in, I sniff the leather as it passes my nose,
A fiery welcome from a 'wannabe' Curtly Ambrose.

I tighten my grip on my trusty blade, here he comes again... 90 miles an hour,
I pick up my Aldred, back lift high, it pitches short, it bounces high
And Aldred connects with staggering power...

Six!
And my innings begins...

Toby Lambert (12)
Newark Academy, New Balderton

The Boy Down Our Street

There is a boy who lives down our street, his eyes are kind of dull.
Whenever you look at him it is like staring into his soul.
It is cold and it's dark.
It's scary and grim.
No wonder everybody keeps avoiding him.
Does he see light?
Does he have fun?
Do his eyes even catch the sun?
I wonder what he sees when looking at a falling leaf?
Does he see a pattern? Or a lost part of a tree...?
People say, "A wave of happiness is coming his way!"
But he says, "There's a shield of darkness getting in the way."
I was walking down the street face up to the sky, the boy was walking towards me, but I did not want to say hi.
Instead I avoided him, like everybody else.
I did feel guilty but that's what I had to do.

There is a boy who lives down our street, his eyes are kind of dull.
Whenever you look at him it is like staring into his soul...

Macie Welshman (12)
Newark Academy, New Balderton

Life Of A Teenager

Things start to change
Suddenly you flick the book's pages
You go to the climax
The problem has occurred now you just need to discover the
solution
Your brain gets packed with confusion
It gushes through your head
You want it to disappear
But it is a lot tougher than you think
You slowly start to sink
Your brain gets filled with things you never encountered
before
You and your emotions start an eternal war
Trying to fight them away
They control your day
Time to check social media you say
People with the perfect body
Perfect life
You want to live like that
Your brain makes you think you are not beautiful enough
It's making your life feel rough
You need to look in the mirror and remind yourself that
you're beautiful
Never let anyone bring you down
Be around people who make you feel amazing
You have made it to the falling action

Emotions are under control
You have earned your goal
Well done!

Libby Duddles (13)
Newark Academy, New Balderton

Donald Trump

D ays go by, I'm sat up here watching down on the world.

O n my throne, I feel at home all the proletarians just go roam

N ever in need for entertainment, Twitter is my arrangement

A ll scientific information is deluded, it will be my opinion that is suited.

L ying is my strategy, that's why they all come after me

D oubt from others, no need to stress, Corona is fake and I'm the best.

T hey say I'm sexist, but I am not, women just need to watch what they say

R ace is fine, but only if your race is mine.

U nusual times means I have to play with their minds.

M exico can stay away, but It's up to you to pay

P ower is the solution to my life, if you vote for me this country will strive.

Amelia Smith-Cowling (13)

Newark Academy, New Balderton

Change Thanking

C hange can mean very different things
H ow can we make change? You could
A pply to the navy or collage to save your country
N othing or nobody should not feel ecstatic
G reat thank yous to key workers and the NHS
E verybody has done exceedingly well.

T his year has been a year of surprises
H aving spent time inside has brought more people together
A nimals are still dying and no one can do anything about it
N ever in my life have I seen something deadlier than this year
K eep up the epic work trying to stop it
I want things to go back
N ever give up
G reat work.

Ella Gilfillan (12)
Newark Academy, New Balderton

King Of The Jungle

I am known as king of the jungle
I can be brown, tan or white
There is only one male in my pack
That's me, but I had a fight.

I am a dangerous carnivore
I live in a grassy plain
You would easily recognise me
With my huge fluffy mane

By day I am a sleeper
Unless I smell my prey
For antelope, buffalo or deer
I could stay awake all day

At night I have powers
I can see in the dark
I sneak up on my meal
Like an early morning lark

I am fierce, I am wild
I am also very clever
Would you want to cross me?
I guess the answer is never!

Cameron-Lee Dunn (12)

Newark Academy, New Balderton

Football

I despise football,
I would rather go shopping at the mall.
Mainly because of the time it takes,
It's so boring for heaven's sake.

The club makes money off my attendance.
Though I would much rather use my independence,
To do something good for the planet,
Then to watch Utd play with my aunty Janet.

I love football,
It's so much fun with Aunty Janet and Uncle Paul.
The best things are the cheers and chants,
Some of them make me laugh, it's excellent bants.
My older brother's quite mad,
When I come home all sad.
That my team lost,
'Cause I didn't put in that final cross.

Jamie Sanders (12)
Newark Academy, New Balderton

Lost

Today was my first day at school
I went to my first two classes
Which were science then English
Now it's breaktime I want to explore the school
I'm Tony by the way
I get lost on the fourth level
I don't know where the stairs are
I look everywhere but can't find them
I even try looking for students
But there are none
I walk around the corner and find a teacher
And ask for some stairs
"Right there," she points whilst speaking
And down I go
I'm not lost anymore
I remember I have a map in my backpack
I am never lost again.

Nathan Binns (12)
Newark Academy, New Balderton

The Crazy World Of Social Media

Don't be afraid of life, be yourself

For TikTok you can dance
You want to be like everyone else,
Phew! Good thing about TikTok is you get another chance.

For Instagram you take pictures and try to look cool,
But you're only making yourself look like a fool!

Lazily lounging upstairs on my phone,
My wrecked room is the best place to be,
Slow as a sloth, can't be bothered to go downstairs
Will text Mum to ask: what's for tea?

Snapchat, Whatsapp, YouTube, group text
I spend all day keeping up on these apps,
I don't want to be the one left behind
They might talk about me next...

Rhiannon Brown (12)
Newark Academy, New Balderton

Humans

Humans came and everything changed
They destroyed our home
There's no more hope
Humans polluted the air
There's barely any clean air
Plastic is our biggest enemy
We think it's part of our food
Water is no longer blue
It's now covered in trash
Humans are killing us for no reason
We don't attack them
They say we are dangerous
But really they are
These cities were once our home
For what things did we do
To deserve this type of thing?

Oliwia Wojajczyk
Newark Academy, New Balderton

Who Is Trump?

Who is Trump to say cancelling on WHO is right?
Who is Trump to say global warming is a hoax?
Who is Trump to say a wall is right?
Who is Trump to say that Obama was wrong?
Who is Trump to say withdrawing from the Paris Agreement was right?
Who is Trump to say America is full?
Who is Trump to say that Coronavirus will go away like a miracle?
Who is Trump to say guns are right?
Who is voting for a man with these views?
Who am I to say he is wrong or right?

Gracie Watkin (12)
Newark Academy, New Balderton

My Dream

To be the best you've got to be better than the rest
Set goals, work towards them to be the best
Keep focused on mind and body
And don't be distracted by anybody
Work hard, train hard, eat well
Have passion in your heart
For the sport that you love
Use each failure to drive you on
To achieve your aim
To be the best
Sacrifice is part of the deal
It's all worth it in the end
When the dream is achieved!

Fin Charles (12)
Newark Academy, New Balderton

While I Sleep

While I sleep blue lights whirl and large machines beep,
While I sleep lives saved and lives at risk,
While I sleep in a healthy home full of love,
Lives saved and lives at risk.
While I sleep no thoughts race,
While I sleep blue lights whirl and large machines beep
Thoughts race and hearts race,
What would we do without these heroes?
Take a moment to think as those blue lights whirl and large
machines beep.

Olivia Sayers (12)
Newark Academy, New Balderton

Imprisoned

Lonely, damp and small,
The door opened with a creak and mouldy breakfast was served...
Mouldy cold toast was on a plate served with nothing but water,
I sat in my lumpy bed and ate sorrowfully,
It was disgusting,
I am isolated cold and alone
I started to question myself, why I am here...?
What had I done wrong...?
Why am I treated like this...?
How long am I in here for...?
Am I guilty or not...?

Ryley Picker (12)
Newark Academy, New Balderton

Monkey Business

Swinging through the jungle
Going tree to tree
I smell bananas
So I must go and see

I climb up the tallest tree
To see what there is to eat
I fall and swing through the sky
With other monkeys to beat

I spy bananas in the tree
So jump and leap to see
Other monkeys I push away
So yummy bananas for my tea.

Ellis Hall (12)
Newark Academy, New Balderton

Bullying

I'm so unhappy,
Because the other kids bully me,
It's getting harder to get up,
To go to school and do the work.

They shout, scream and hurt me,
Because I'm not one of the family,
It's time to take a stand,
Against the bullies and be,
The better man,
It's time to go all in,
I can't let the bullies win!

Jamie Briers (12)
Newark Academy, New Balderton

Sporty, Sporty, Sporty

His name is Jack,
He runs on a track.
Slides down a slope,
Scoring goals he hopes.
Going round the bend,
Hockey sticks to mend.
Big sails crossing seas,
Hopefully they don't freeze.
Tiny holes to get,
Sure some will sweat.
Not doing any work,
Show that he is no nerd.
Getting low scores,
Means doing more chores.

Tyler Dodd (13)
Newark Academy, New Balderton

Lion Cub

His innocent eyes flutter,
He cuddles up to his father and drifts off slowly to sleep,
His mother heads out to catch food,
Clueless of the danger they are about to await.

The small pride left are asleep,
Vulnerable and unaware
The females return with their bounty
The small pride awakes, you join in the feast.

Emma Taylor (12)
Newark Academy, New Balderton

When I Drop By

When I drop, I drift to the ground
When I drift to the ground, I tumble
When I tumble, I get stuck
When I get stuck, I stay
The animals come
When I get carried away, I am harmful
When I am harmful, I kill
I am all around you and never go away. Why?

Daisy Pounder (13)
Newark Academy, New Balderton

The Red Flower

This summer was hotter than ever before
Animals died of dehydration
The eucalyptus was crispy and no longer juicy
That was when the fires came.

The red flower blossoms around me, enveloping me with
heat
I leap from tree to tree, passing echidna, cassowary, more
The life sucked out of them
All my home in devastation
Trees ablaze
It is only then I realise, I have nowhere to go.

I wander through the wasteland that was once my majestic
home
Trees burnt to ashes, if strong enough to withstand the
heat,
burnt and blackened skeletons
I stopped
I was hungry
I searched, but there was no eucalyptus
I stopped
Paralysed
Too weak to move
Then, like all the others in this barren wasteland,
I perished.

Raven Coward (11)
Settle College, Giggleswick

Before You Went

We loved once, we did again,
You promised you wouldn't leave,
Now I'm left here to grieve,
I remember the flowers, chocolates and cards
The love you gave yards on yard
You were my one in a million,
I could find you in a trillion
Our love was bold,
You were there as we grew old
Now I know our chance has gone
But I still love you by the ton
My heart is broke
My heart is shattered
But you're the only one that still mattered
Don't leave, I plead
On this day, of Valentine's Day
Before you went, I was one
Before you went, we loved
All before you went.

Lucy Mason (12)
Settle College, Giggleswick

52

It's thirty-two years from 2020
There's even too much plastic for our needs.
We have a million more than plenty,
We don't have any room to plant our seeds.
I have rushed across the plastic bridge
From the English Channel to the coast,
I crossed to an American ridge
And there he was, horns 'n' all,
The Devil's host.
He stood there waiting and watching,
Dead still he was, ready to pounce.
I froze, dark magic upon me, my breath catching,
It cost me every ounce.
He was the Devil's host.

Willow Coward (11)
Settle College, Giggleswick

Love In A Day

All's fair in love and war
Through the world in a door
Last the love of a couple
Away from the trouble.

All's fair in love and war
Away from all the sores
Away from the blast
To escape the horrible past.

All's fair in love and war
Where no one's been before
In a world we create ourselves
Away from the pressure valves.

All's fair in love and war
Where nobody cares what you be
If anyone loves you, let free
It's a miracle.

Henry Pain (12)
Settle College, Giggleswick

Candlelight Love

Romeo, look at me
Let me see your smile and hear your laugh
Because you're the brightest light I see
The candle that isn't blown out by a draught.

Juliet, stop staring at me
My heart can't stop beating
I know I'm not the hottest boy you see
My love has meaning.

You are the one
The candle I never knew I had
My love for you has never gone
The brightest candle I've had
The candle I love.

Emily Scott (13)
Settle College, Giggleswick

To Heaven I Fly

This war is no game,
Just fights and flames,
But as the blood pumped through my veins
A shot was fired and I felt pain
I won't die in vain
I told myself
But in good health.

Aaden James Ford (11)
Settle College, Giggleswick

The Blue Whale's Death

I am a mammal,
You might think I'm smart
I'm not, I don't know anything
As you throw that plastic in the bin
Think of me and my family.

I have seen my family die,
My home destroyed,
My friends all gone,
With that piece of plastic.

It looks like food,
You know it's not,
We do not,
We feed,
It's like food,
But,
We die, we rot.

We are found on the news,
Plastic inside,
Makes you feel sad,
But you keep on going
Just throwing, throwing
You like your plastic
We like our lives.

I am just a blue whale
A whale with a mind of its own,
Alone,
Trying to survive in a sea of plastic.

Why kill us?
What would happen if your kids ate plastic?
Why should we become extinct?
Home,
Home is no longer there
My life is destroyed
Think of me as you don't recycle.

Ben Charlie Sharpe (14)
The JCB Academy, Rocester

Teenager's Nightmare

My life turned out to be a reality,
Small things can tick me off
All the anger inside me boiled up
I feel like,
I feel like,
Choking my head, chains of insults strangle me,
Prisoners in my head, banging on the walls of my skull,
How can one person not even claim liberty over themselves?
Why is it so difficult for them to understand?
Can they really see how much the scars inside me will taunt
me for the rest of my life?
Every day, the curtains of hate engulf me,
As the sheer stubbornness of my own fate can penetrate the
hopes
Of attending a class where the teacher hasn't heard of me
Mood swings are things beyond my control
Talk to the screaming party that was captured inside me
Do you think I had any choice of what I've become?
Or are you masking the truth that will never become a
reality?
Anger, sadness, everything but fear,
How many times do I have to say
I hate the world and the world must pay?

Daania Abuthaheer (12)
Wallington High School For Girls, Wallington

Scarlet Paws

Another young one thrown in jail
Large, crimson cuts smothered her blue skin
Like a child drowning, she gasped, and died.

Humans have lost all of their art
Gone, burnt, like what Ray Bradbury penned
All of these protests, simply because the media took every misdemeanour
And inflated it to the size of the world.

Gently, I licked the red mixture, that was intoxicating,
Delicious
Our population would never let a young one suffer like her
Such cruelty would never be thought of
Our leaders would listen, not squash, so we are peaceful in our act
A prison would never exist, for our paws are as clean as cubs.

Slowly, I slipped into the gleaming pipes
That screamed and scratched me
But who am I to worry about my peaceful life
One day
Another one will watch the humans suffer
Because of their brother's ignorance
They will collapse
We will rise.

Bonnie Witter
Wallington High School For Girls, Wallington

This Mirror, Mirror On The Wall

There are many things in a person's home,
Bed, wardrobes and many more,
But there is one that catches eyes,
This mirror, mirror on the wall,

It reveals your secrets,
Your future untold,
It tells you where to put your mascara and all,
It's always there to give a helping hand,
This mirror, mirror on the wall,

Mirrors are different from everything else,
They're quite different from the rest,
They come in all shapes and sizes,
Curved, sharp, big, small,
This mirror, mirror on the wall,

They are found in many different places,
Like storybooks and fairytales,
The wicked stepmother, so vain she is,
Shouting at the poor, old thing
This mirror, mirror on the wall,

This mirror, mirror on the wall,
Helps many people,
Big or small,
That's my duty after all,
'Cause I'm the mirror on the wall.

Sivaranjini Pillai (11)
Wallington High School For Girls, Wallington

The Picturesque Darkness

My eyes blur at the strange sight
Eye-catching but peculiar
The deafening silence then erupts
The ash choking the land
A picturesque view
With dark secrets lying in the undergrowth.

The beautiful, vibrant flower
Portrayed as 'innocent'
It will use its looks to deceive you
A vile creature lives inside it
The soft, gentle butterfly
Is really a terrifying monster
Waiting to jump with its wings.

Our eyes deceive us.

The jaws of death are about to open - I can feel it
I had always known that they would come for me
Ready to leap
But am I ready to fall into the enchantment spell of death?
Now that is the real question
I guess I have to wait for tomorrow to come
Dead or alive...

Jasmine Williams (12)
Wallington High School For Girls, Wallington

Darkness

There's a place that I know
A place full of darkness
A place where people die
Where hatred covers all

Right is always wrong
Wrong is always right
I am the captor
But I am held captive

The people there are distant
And sometimes just not there
Sure, the world's a dark place
But this place is darker, I swear

An endless void of black
A portal straight to hell
The light can never reach it
Nothing's ever well

It's a place full of darkness
An endless void of black
An inferno of perpetual suffering
And guess what? That inferno is my mind.

Ollie Thorneloe (13)
Wallington High School For Girls, Wallington

Politicians

They do not care, they do not see,
They seem to look right through me,
Hearts of stone and minds of wire,
They burn my world on fire.

Angry voices in my head,
All the words that they have said,
Our weak response is lost,
Now we've got to pay the cost.

Gaping jaws, a thousand-feet wide,
Entrance deep and dark,
No one knows what's inside.

A fixed, false smile,
An evil glare,
A million miles,
Without a care.

The carnivore and prey
There's nothing left to say,
The hound has caught the fox,
And then the fox was left to rot.

Beatrix Leeming (11)
Wallington High School For Girls, Wallington

Prey

I run, I jump, I hide, I flee
From pursuers hunting me
Mangy wolves and clever foxes
To tall humans with their boxes.

In this game of hide-and-seek
Rules are broken, so are the meek
So dare to run
Before they come
Run, run, run!

Rabbits, voles, sparrows, wrens
All hiding in their dens
Hunger radiates in the air
Our lives were never fair.

It's all about an eye for an ear
They know that we live here
So we have to run, run, run!

Life is a gamble
The weak ones scramble
The strong ones hunt
For us, their lunch!

Sreeranjini Pillai (11)
Wallington High School For Girls, Wallington

2050

The world's slowly dying
Can you hear nature dying?
Intervention's badly needed,
But sadly, few have heeded.

Our electronic usage,
Is becoming more abusive
We watch television in HD
And yet are blinded to reality.

Plants have lost life,
Because of the strife
We do not fully know,
The harm which we have sown.

The future is here,
Although fraught and unclear
Action must start today,
Or we'll have a grave price to pay.

This could be our future...

Anika Gupta (11)
Wallington High School For Girls, Wallington

YOUNG WRITERS
INFORMATION

We hope you have enjoyed reading this book – and that you will continue to in the coming years.

If you're a young writer who enjoys reading and creative writing, or the parent of an enthusiastic poet or story writer, do visit our website **www.youngwriters.co.uk**. Here you will find free competitions, workshops and games, as well as recommended reads, a poetry glossary and our blog. There's lots to keep budding writers motivated to write!

If you would like to order further copies of this book, or any of our other titles, then please give us a call or order via your online account.

Young Writers
Remus House
Coltsfoot Drive
Peterborough
PE2 9BF
(01733) 890066
info@youngwriters.co.uk

Join in the conversation!
Tips, news, giveaways and much more!

 YoungWritersUK    @YoungWritersCW